SCHOLASTIC

Let's Find Out

My REBUS Reader

I0890032

Get Ready for Winter, Chipmunk!

by Pamela Chanko

SCHOLASTIC INC.

New York Toronto London Auckland Sydney New Delhi Hong Kong

The  gets .

chipmunk nuts

It gets  too.

seeds

It runs back to its  .

burrow

It gets  for a bed.

leaves

The winter  is ready.

burrow

Now there is  . Time to go in!

snow

Sleep well,  .

chipmunk